You Can't Eat Love

Workbook

Resources by Leslie Lindsey Davis

You Can't Eat Love

You Can't Eat Love Workbook

So, I said to myself… Journal

Fit and Food Journal

https://youcanteatlove.com/

Facebook group: You Can't Eat Love

Instagram: you_cant_eat_love

To thank you for reading my book, here is a free quiz:

Find out what kind of healthy eater you are.

https://Info.youcanteatlove.com

How Learning to *Love Yourself*
Can Change Your Relationship with Food

you can't EAT love

LESLIE LINDSEY DAVIS

For more information, email leslie@youcanteatlove.com

ISBN: (print only)

Dedication

Dedicated to:

my parents, who did the best they could.

my sisters, Kathy, Isa, and Allison, who threw lifelines to me just when I needed them most.

my brothers, Bill and Norman, who would come if I called.

my husband, Mike, who is wise enough to not stop me, even though he cannot understand half of my crazy dreams.

my three amazing sons, Philip, Jeffrey, and Matthew, who taught me that there is indeed a difference between boys and girls, and who love me even though they think I am crazy.

my amazing daughters-in-love, Carmen, Elizabeth, and Taylor, whose love for my boys is more than I could have wished for.

Jackie, who met me where I was and helped me believe I could do a little more and then a little more.

Joan Murray (Joan Murray Ministries), who believed I had a story to tell when I didn't even know the story.

With a prayer of thanks to…

God, who knew me before I was born.

Jesus, who kept me on the path.

The Holy Spirit, who gave me the words when I struggled to express myself.

Table of Contents

Introduction 7

Pie is Not Always Just Pie 10

You Can Begin Again With a Trip 13

Pack Your Suitcase 15

It's Not About the Destination 20

If It Were Easy, Everyone Would Do It 24

If it were easy, everyone would do it 29

No Should Zone 35

Back to Our Regularly Scheduled Program 40

Cheater, Cheater, Pumpkin Eater 45

Trigger is Not just the name of Roy Roger's Horse 49

How Do We Get From Here to There 54

Greens, Greens, And More Greens 58

To Move Or Not To Move, That Is The Question 62

I Don't Want To Be The Rock 66

There Is A Reason They Give Stars To Kindergartners 70

Eeny, Meeny, Miney, Moe 74

Progress Not Perfection 79

You Don't Have To Do This Alone 83

Very end? No, just the beginning 87

Introduction

This workbook is designed to help you dig really deep into yourself and discover the real you or your BFFITWWW (best friend in the whole wide world). By discovering and uncovering who you really are AND what you really desire in life; you can learn to love yourself, change your relationship with food and live your best life. I will be with you every step of the way.

Each chapter is divided into five sections.

- Section 1 – So, I was saying… summarizes the main points of the chapter in the book

- Section 2 – And now your turn… asks you questions and provides space for your responses and reflections. This is where the hard work is done. You can go over this section as many times as you need to. I like to pick up a different color pen so I can see where my responses have changed or expanded (remember – you do you 😊).

- Section 3 – Check your suitcase – as we are traveling, we pick up tools and other items to help us on the journey. The newer items are at the top of the list. The same list can be found at the end of each chapter in your book.

- Section 4 – Life Hacks – these are tips and tricks that I picked up on my journey, others that I borrowed from wiser people and just general random information that I hope will help you. Again, these are in your book.

- Section 5 – Jackie's Corner – tips from the amazing Jackie (a certified trainer) to help you discover your best workout program.

- Section 6 – Travel Guides – This is where I have highlighted different books, resources, and other material I think will support you on your journey. Just as a travel guide can give you more detail about the city or place you are visiting; these resources can help you dig deeper into you and your journey.

This journey is all about learning how to handle the traffic jams in life, so we stay in the car, do not park, do not get out and (most importantly) do not walk home.

Buckle up and safe travels!

Leslie Lindsey Davis

Katy, Texas

Section 1

Why Didn't You Tell Me in the First Place

"A journey of a thousand miles begins with a single step."
Attributed to Lau-Tzu

Chapter 1

Pie is Not Always Just Pie

So, I was saying...

Lies I told myself:

- Diet drinks cancel out the empty calories in chocolate candy
- Broken cookies and food eaten from someone else's plate doesn't have any calories
- Food eaten without anyone knowing you ate it does not have any calories
- Raw cookie dough does not have any calories – baking them activates the calories
- Pans were not properly sized, and I could not put the "extra" in the trash
- Bites and fat cut from the meat does not have any calories
- I had a rodent problem
- I was broken and I just needed a pill to fix me

And now, your turn...

Mark, underline, or highlight any of the above lies you have told yourself.

Now, write out any other lies you have told yourself.

_____
_____
_____
_____
_____
_____
_____
_____

What's in your suitcase?

- Snap a photo – post it to the You Can't Eat Love Facebook page
- Join the private You Can't Eat Love Facebook group
- Workbook (www.youcanteatlove.com/workbook)
- *So, I said to myself…* Journal (you can get it here https://www.amazon.com/dp/B08NZ3Y7GF)
- Pens
- Highlighters

Life Hacks

- This journey is about choosing you. Decide on a time of day you can spend quality time with you. Either create a reminder in your phone or write it on your calendar. If you decide early in the morning while the house is quiet is the best time, commit to setting your alarm to get up just ten minutes early. Say to yourself – *I'm choosing me*. Write it down. *The Miracle Morning* by Hal Elrod[i] is a great resource to help you get started.

- Start noticing how you're speaking to yourself. Notice how other people are speaking to you. Go to www.youcanteatlove.com/journal to order the *So, I said to myself…* journal and download sample pages so you can begin having conversations with yourself.

- Inner voices (the ones that don't speak nicely to you) – I call them monsters, the critic, and hamsters on wheels. Feel free to substitute whatever you call them – BUT do name them. Also, along on this journey are two four-year old children (a brat and a scared one), two parents (critical and kind), and your very best friend in the whole wide world.

- Life jackets – sometimes I will toss you a life jacket or you will toss one to me. Sometimes we need one because we're tired of swimming and just need to float a bit, rest, and get ready to swim again. It's ok to grab one and hold on. You don't have to give it back. You can keep it for the next time you need to rest.

- I have lots of sayings and expressions, please feel free to use them, modify them or let me know that it didn't work for you.

- I tell a lot of stories and I hope you learn a little something from my stories. *BUT* I really want to hear your stories. I can learn a lot from you too. Remember, we're going to be traveling together. Won't be much fun if I'm doing all the talking. You can tell me your stories on You Can't Eat Love Facebook or leslie@youcanteatlove.com

- At the end of each chapter, I will have tips and tricks that I have made up as I have gone along this journey. I hope you find them useful.

- I will be including links to all types of information, questionnaires, and resources. If you've not downloaded the workbook yet www.youcanteatlove.com/workbook. You can also order a hard copy.

- Also, you will get a few words from the amazing Jackie about how to add activity and exercise into your life at your pace

Jackie says

- Start slow

Travel Guides

- *So, I said to myself...* Journal - available on Amazon
  www.amazon.com/dp/B08NZ3Y7GF
- *Fit and Food Journal* - available on Amazon
  https://www.amazon.com/dp/1736232207

Chapter 2

You Can Begin Again With a Trip

So, I was saying...

- You will learn to speak kindly to yourself
- Create plans of action
- Practice for situations that involve food
- Learn how to ask for what you need
- Learn to fill the "myself-sized" hole in your heart
- Learn you are never alone

And now, your turn...

Where are you going to drive your stake in the ground?

_____

_____

_____

_____

_____

_____

_____

_____

_____

_____

_____

_____

What's in your suitcase?

- Stake
- Hammer
- www.youcanteatlove.com
- Snap a photo – post it to the You Can't Eat Love Facebook page
- Join the private You Can't Eat Love Facebook group
- Workbook
- *So, I said to myself...* Journal
- Pens
- Highlighters

Life Hacks

- Lose the word diet from your vocabulary. Think about the last time you went on a diet. How did you really feel? What you are choosing to do is discover a new lifestyle. A lifestyle that you can live out the rest of your life. One that fits you and not the other way around.

Jackie says

- Meet you where you are
- Drink lots of water

Travel Guides

- Closed You Can't Eat Love Facebook group

Chapter 3

Pack Your Suitcase

So, I was saying…

- You will discover WHY you are on this journey
- You will learn about oxygen masks and why you need one

And now, your turn…

Finding you so you can discover your why

1. What excites you? Think about things you like to do and places you like to go.

   _____

   _____

   _____

2. On a scale of 1–5 (1 is extremely unhappy and 5 is extremely happy), rate how you feel about the following areas of your life:
   Health _____ Friends _____ Family _____
   Recreation (Fun) _____ Personal Growth _____

3. Now write why you gave each of those areas the rating you did. Be honest. Remember, no one else is going to see this unless you decide to share it with them.
   Health

   _____

   _____

   _____

   Friends

   _____

   _____

   _____

Family

_____
_____
_____

Recreation (Fun)

_____
_____
_____

Growth

_____
_____
_____

4. What do you believe you cannot do? (Yes, losing weight can be one of those things.)

_____
_____
_____

5. What would your life look like if you believed you could do those things? (If you need to, channel your thoughts toward The Little Engine That Could by Watty Piper.)

_____
_____
_____

6. What was your relationship with food ten years ago?

_____
_____
_____

7. What is your relationship with food today? What changed? Why do you think it changed?

_____
_____
_____

8. What are your fears and why? List as many fears as you can think of. Failure and success can both be fears. I am afraid of

_____
_____
_____

because (Keep going! You've got this!)

_____
_____
_____

9. Pick one of your fears and think about how it would feel to act against just that one fear. What would that look like?

_____
_____
_____

10. List the challenges you have had over the past year.

_____
_____
_____

11. What did you learn about yourself from these challenges?

_____
_____
_____

12. Following is my long-time mantra: I don't want to be 80 years old, sitting on my front porch in my rocker and saying I wish I would have…_____

_____
_____

13. Now it is your turn to fill in the blank…

_____
_____
_____

14. Fill in these blanks: My name is _____ I am (not a job title or diet failure) _____ In the past, I have (had what kind of relationship/belief system about food)

_____
_____
_____

,but now I am ready to (describe what kind of relationship you want with yourself, not food)

_____
_____
_____

This is important to me because (nothing to do with your weight, another person, or an event)

_____

_____

_____

_____

_____

WHY I want to reclaim myself matters. I am important to me.

You can go to www.youcanteatlove.com/mywhy to see the interview about *my*

WHY.

What is your WHY? (write it out here) Were you surprised by what you discovered about your WHY?

_____

_____

_____

_____

_____

_____

_____

Write down at least 3 affirmations or quotes that encourage you. Copy them onto index cards and put them where you can read them at least once a day.

_____

_____

_____

_____

_____

_____

_____

What's in your suitcase?

- Oxygen mask
- WHY
- Friedrich Nietzche quote
- Photo of you
- Index cards
- Stake
- Hammer
- www.youcanteatlove.com
- Snap a photo – post it to the You Can't Eat Love Facebook page

- Join the private You Can't Eat Love Facebook group
- Workbook
- *So, I said to myself...* Journal
- Pens
- Highlighters

Life Hacks

- Each month, as I plan for the month ahead, I write this same note to myself on my planner: "I'm MY #1 priority". This is a code I have come up with to gently remind myself of *my WHY* without sharing with anyone else. You can borrow my note or come up with a few of your own.
- I copied my *WHY* onto several index cards and keep them in strategic places (like my planner, my inspirational reading books) so I can remind myself *why* I'm on this journey. I don't leave it out for the general public to see.
- After you create your *WHY*, find a photo of yourself that makes you smile at the memory of when the photo was taken. Make copies of that photo and put them with your copies of your *WHY*. I want you to recall the feeling the memory reminds you of. Drop a copy in your suitcase while you're at it!

Jackie says

- Find your WHY
- Take progress pictures

Travel Guides

- Closed You Can't Eat Love Facebook group

Chapter 4

It's Not About the Destination

So, I was saying...

- A trip is not about the destination
- Focus is not the end
- It's about the journey
- Make preparations
- Be ready to be flexible

And now, your turn...

What is the furthest you have ever traveled?

_____
_____
_____
_____

How did you plan that trip?

_____
_____
_____

Why did you go on that trip?

_____
_____
_____
_____

What did you pack?

_____

_____

_____

_____

What did you do to get ready to go on that trip? (pet sitter, mail etc)

_____

_____

_____

_____

Where do you think you want to go on this trip? (write it in very small print on the very last page of this workbook)

_____

_____

_____

_____

What's in your suitcase?

- Trash bags
- Oxygen mask
- WHY
- Friedrich Nietzsche quote
- Photo of you
- Index cards
- Stake
- Hammer
- www.youcanteatlove.com

- Snap a photo – post it to the You Can't Eat Love Facebook page
- Join the private You Can't Eat Love Facebook group
- Workbook
- *So, I said to myself...* Journal
- Pens
- Highlighters

Life Hacks

- The greatest gift you can give yourself as you begin this journey is to clean out your pantry, fridge, and freezer. Get rid of any foods that cause problems for you. Make a list of some fresh items you can substitute for what you're eliminating and make a quick trip to the store. Only pick up what is on your list.

Jackie says

- Don't skip warmups
- Remember results take time

Travel Guides

- Adult BMI Calculator

Section 2
I Am Seeking to Find

Never, never, never give up.
Winston Churchill

Chapter 5

If It Were Easy, Everyone Would Do It

So, I was saying...

- Keep your travel plans to yourself
- I can only do something about me
- Alone together – not together alone
- Sabotaging people and plans to handle them

And now, your turn...

The last time you told someone you were going on a diet, what did they say?

_____
_____
_____

What were you thinking as you listened to their comments? How did you really feel?

_____
_____
_____
_____
_____

What did you do next?

_____
_____
_____
_____

How did you feel?

_____
_____
_____
_____

On an index card write – I can only do something about myself. I am not in control or in charge of anyone else. I am only in charge of me. – put it where you can see it daily.

List of sabotaging people and how they sabotage you

Person	How

Now, you have identified these people and know how *they* are creating a traffic jam on your journey. Let's make a plan for what we are going to say or do the next time we are with them. (Flag or mark this page so you can easily refer to your plan).

_____

_____

_____

_____

_____

_____

_____

_____

_____

List of kind souls and how they push food

Person	How

Now, you have identified these people and know how *they* are creating a traffic jam on your journey. Let's make a plan for what we are going to say or do the next time we are with them. (Flag or mark this page so you can easily refer to your plan).

_____

_____

_____

_____

_____

_____

After you make your plans, start practicing. This is how it gets easier to handle the traffic jams. You're not looking for perfect. Just looking to stay in your car, not get out and not walk home.

What's in your suitcase?

- Idea about your destination
- Plan for sabotagers
- Plan for food pushers
- Trash bags
- Oxygen mask
- WHY
- Friedrich Nietzsche quote
- Photo of you
- Index cards
- Stake
- Hammer
- www.youcanteatlove.com

- Snap a photo – post it to the You Can't Eat Love Facebook page
- Join the private You Can't Eat Love Facebook group
- Workbook
- *So, I said to myself…* Journal
- Pens
- Highlighters

Life Hacks

- Alone together, not together alone. Remember.

Jackie says

- Do workouts you enjoy
- Think of exercise as taking great care of yourself and not punishment

Travel Guides

- A playlist
- Podcasts

Chapter 6

If it were easy, everyone would do it

So, I was saying...

A traffic jam is anything that keeps you from moving forward, right? When you are driving somewhere and there is a wreck or broken-down vehicle, the traffic slows to a crawl or even stops. When we are traveling the road of a new lifestyle, the same thing can happen. We are not losing weight or inches as fast as we think we should (we will talk about that word later). Then we allow doubt to creep in and start thinking we are failing (we will talk about that word too) so we decide that this "isn't working" and we give up on our new lifestyle.

Or a food that you don't have a very good relationship with (like chocolate for me) comes into your house and you start struggling to keep from eating it. That is a traffic jam too.

A traffic jam is ANYTHING or ANYONE that keeps you from moving forward as fast as you "think" you should be (there's that word again). It is anything or anyone that causes you to second guess your choice of a new lifestyle.

And now, your turn...

Traffic Jams
What are some traffic jams you might run into?

_____

_____

_____

_____

_____

What can you do when you run into a traffic jam? (take a 5-10 minute walk, switch from a banana to an apple for snack, now your turn!)

_____

_____

_____

_____

_____

What are some conversations you have with yourself? (After you write them down, read them out loud so you can hear how you are speaking to yourself)

_____

_____

_____

_____

_____

Read these conversations again – this time shout STOP! as you read each one

Look back at these conversations and write down what you would say to your BFF

_____

_____

_____

_____

_____

_____

_____

How did that feel?

_____
_____
_____
_____
_____
_____

So, I said to myself Journal has space in it to write down kind thoughts you have towards yourself.

_____
_____
_____

Family philosophy about food (be honest with yourself about not only food, but the emotions)

What was your family's rules/view with snacks?

_____
_____
_____
_____
_____

What were special occasions like with your family?

_____
_____
_____
_____
_____

What were everyday meals like with your family?

_____
_____
_____
_____
_____

What are you surprised you discovered?

_____
_____
_____
_____
_____
_____
_____
_____
_____

What do you want YOUR philosophy about food to be?

_____
_____
_____
_____
_____
_____
_____
_____
_____

Imagine you are at the next family gathering. What do you want to do that is different from the past? How will you feel?

_____
_____
_____
_____
_____
_____
_____
_____
_____

What's in your suitcase?

- Google maps
- Locks
- "Traffic Jam" written on an index card
- From www.youcanteatlove.com website, print off the "Stay" card
- Book of positive affirmations
- Seasoning
- Forgiveness
- Choices
- Community
- STOP
- Idea about your destination
- Plan for sabotagers
- Plan for food pushers
- Trash bags
- Oxygen mask

- WHY
- Friedrich Nietzsche quote
- Photo of you
- Index cards
- Stake
- Hammer
- www.youcanteatlove.com
- Snap a photo – post it to the You Can't Eat Love Facebook page
- Join the private You Can't Eat Love Facebook group
- Workbook
- *So, I said to myself…* Journal
- Pens
- Highlighters

Life Hacks

- You just have to be
- Choose – don't give away your power

Jackie says

- Fall in love with the process
- Don't weigh every day

Travel Guides

- A playlist
- Podcasts
- *So, I said to myself...* Journal
- *ANEW Spiritual Awakening: 31 Day Christian Devotional*[ii] (available on Amazon)
- www.hallmark.com

Chapter 7

No Should Zone

So, I was saying...

Let's look at the definition of "should" again.
- used to indicate obligation, duty, or correctness, typically when criticizing someone's actions.

There's that whole criticizing thing again. Now, right now, I want you to commit to not shoulding on yourself (or anyone else) anymore. We will begin reframing these comments, so they help you on your journey.

And now, your turn...

Shoulding
Who are the people in your life that like to should all over you?

_____

_____

_____

_____

_____

How do you feel when they begin those sentences "You should..."?_____

_____

_____

_____

_____

What would you really like to say to them?

_____
_____
_____
_____

Now, time to be honest. When do _YOU_ should all over yourself?

_____
_____
_____
_____

How do you feel when you are busy shoulding all over yourself?

_____
_____
_____
_____

Let's think about how your bff would talk to you and reframe those statements you are making to yourself.

_____
_____
_____
_____
_____
_____
_____
_____

Since you have practiced, let's think about how you can reframe (and yes, I do mean out loud to the person who made the comment to you) the shoulding comments someone else makes to you. Remember, you are not going to give away your power.

_____
_____
_____
_____
_____
_____
_____
_____

How did that feel?

_____

_____

_____

_____

_____

_____

_____

_____

What's in your suitcase?

- No Should Zone t-shirt and poster
- Your power
- Google maps
- Locks
- "Traffic Jam" written on an index card
- From www.youcanteatlove.com website, print off the "Stay" card
- Book of positive affirmations
- Seasoning
- Forgiveness
- Choices
- Community
- STOP
- Idea about your destination
- Plan for sabotagers
- Plan for food pushers
- Trash bags
- Oxygen mask
- WHY
- Friedrich Nietzsche quote
- Photo of you
- Index cards
- Stake
- Hammer
- www.youcanteatlove.com
- Snap a photo – post it to the You Can't Eat Love Facebook page
- Join the private You Can't Eat Love Facebook group
- Workbook
- *So, I said to myself...* Journal
- Pens
- Highlighters

Life Hacks

- Reframing comments we make to ourselves helps keep our car driving forward in those new ruts on that muddy road
- How many times did you hear a phrase that went something like this "you should (see that ugly word?) be ashamed of yourself." Think about how you felt. Delete that phrase – you are wonderful, kind, smart and beautiful. Nowhere in the description of you is shame.
- Toss "shame" out of the window along with "ashamed". Positive words filling your mind will help you on this journey.

Jackie says

- Fall in love with the process
- Don't weigh every day

Travel Guides

- No Should Zone!

Chapter 8

Back to Our Regularly Scheduled Program

So, I was saying...

- <u>First things first!</u>
  Stand up and cheer for how you are changing AND taking care of yourself!
- Feelings – what's really eating you?
- Your BFFITWWW
- You can only lie to me and myself – I sees everything
- Photo of yourself for the beginning of the trip

And now, your turn...

Now, back to work –

Make a list of your feelings (it is ok if you don't list very many, you can always add to the list)

_____

_____

_____

_____

_____

_____

_____

_____

_____

Circle or mark the feelings that scare you

Be honest – circle or mark (with a different color of pen/pencil) which ones did you use food to quiet or comfort you_____

_____
_____
_____

Which emotion do you think will be the hardest to "sit in"?

_____
_____
_____
_____

Why?

_____
_____
_____
_____

Now, when an emotion – like sad – shows up and I really don't want to feel it. My first clue I am running from it is I start seeking and searching for something to eat. I have learned to recognize this so I will start by asking myself a question. "What is really going on?" "What are you afraid will happen if you just feel this?" "Can you take a few breaths?" "Can you tell me why you are feeling _____? I really want to know." Sometimes, I have to sit down with pen and paper and write it out so I can get it out of my head and that will slow down the waves (remember the life jacket?) I am not going to lie to you, sometimes my emotions override my bff and then nothing is safe. I forgive myself, do my best to comfort myself and move on.

Now, your turn – what will be your plan of action when these hard emotions show up? Mark this page so you can refer to it every day. Remember, practice is how we get prepared. Not looking for perfect, just prepared.

_____
_____
_____
_____
_____
_____

Tell yourself how proud you are of yourself! High fives all around! How does it feel to have a plan?

_____
_____
_____
_____
_____
_____
_____
_____

Remember all the lies I was telling myself? Remember you marked my list and added your own? Now, I want you to talk directly to me and myself. They are only trying to keep you safe and happy. I want you to tell them you forgive them, and you will be ok. Tell them how grateful you are to them and WHY you will be ok.

_____
_____
_____
_____
_____
_____
_____
_____
_____
_____
_____
_____
_____
_____
_____
_____
_____

What's in your suitcase?

- Megaphone (for louder cheering!)
- Tissues
- Full length photo

- Album set up in your phone or on your computer where you will store your "becoming you" photos
- No Should Zone t-shirt and poster
- Your power
- Google maps
- Locks
- "Traffic Jam" written on an index card
- From www.youcanteatlove.com website, print off the "Stay" card
- Book of positive affirmations
- Seasoning
- Forgiveness
- Choices

- Community
- STOP
- Idea about your destination
- Plan for sabotagers
- Plan for food pushers
- Trash bags
- Oxygen mask
- WHY
- Friedrich Nietzsche quote
- Photo of you
- Index cards
- Stake
- Hammer
- www.youcanteatlove.com
- Snap a photo – post it to the You Can't Eat Love Facebook page
- Join the private You Can't Eat Love Facebook group
- Workbook
- *So, I said to myself…* Journal
- Pens
- Highlighters

Life Hacks

- "Oh, well" became a phrase I used when I would make not so great choices that I really did not want to make. Sometimes the emotions would override my logic and as soon as I understood what had happened, I would say "oh, well" instead of beating myself up. Sometimes, "oh, well" is all I could get out. I prefer to forgive myself but sometimes, "oh, well" is enough.

Jackie says

- Be consistent
- Make a date with yourself

Travel Guides

- A playlist that will either comfort you or lift your spirits WHEN you want to be comforted

Chapter 9

Cheater, Cheater, Pumpkin Eater

So, I was saying...

- No cheating – only choices
- Three kinds of choices
- Forgiving yourself

And now, your turn...

Think about when you use the word "cheat"

What are you saying to yourself?

_____

_____

_____

_____

_____

_____

_____

_____

How do you really feel when you use the word "cheat" to describe what you are eating?

_____

_____

_____

_____

_____

Next time, what can you say to yourself?

_____
_____
_____
_____
_____
_____
_____
_____

How will you feel?

_____
_____
_____
_____
_____
_____
_____
_____

Remember, there are only three ways to cheat and none of them involve food or eating. Roll down your window, toss it out of the car, and don't look back!

_____
_____
_____
_____
_____
_____
_____

What's in your suitcase?

- Choice – great choice, good choice, not so great choice
- Megaphone (for louder cheering!)
- Tissues
- Full length photo
- Album set up in your phone or on your computer where you will store your "becoming you" photos
- No Should Zone t-shirt and poster
- Your power
- Google maps
- Locks
- "Traffic Jam" written on an index card
- From www.youcanteatlove.com website, print off the "Stay" card
- Book of positive affirmations
- Seasoning
- Forgiveness
- Choices
- Community
-
- STOP
- Idea about your destination
- Plan for sabotagers
- Plan for food pushers
- Trash bags
- Oxygen mask
- WHY
- Friedrich Nietzsche quote
- Photo of you
- Index cards
- Stake
- Hammer
- www.youcanteatlove.com
- Snap a photo – post it to the You Can't Eat Love Facebook page
- Join the private You Can't Eat Love Facebook group
- Workbook
- *So, I said to myself...* Journal
- Pens
- Highlighters

Life Hacks

- On this journey we want to surround ourselves with thoughts and words that encourage us, especially when we hit a traffic jam. "Cheat" and "will power" are not helpful. Maybe you can think of a few more. Write them down and throw them out of the window too!

Jackie says

- Put yourself first
- Learn to foam roll and stretch (YouTube had great videos)

Travel Guides

- A pen to mark out words in your dictionary

Chapter 10

Trigger is Not just the name of Roy Roger's Horse

So, I was saying...

- Mind travel
- Strategies for triggers
- Celebration and gatherings with friends and family planning

And now, your turn...

What are your triggers?

_____

_____

_____

_____

_____

_____

_____

What do you think and how do you feel when you "meet" these triggers?

_____

_____

_____

_____

Are you trying to recapture or relive something? If yes, describe it to yourself.

_____

_____

_____

_____

Right now, take a moment and write down how you are going to recognize a trigger.

_____

_____

_____

_____

Now, I want you to come up with a plan of action for when you run into a trigger. Mark this page so you can refer to it and practice each day. Remember to practice kindness and understanding. Driving down that muddy road, very slowly. You've got this.

_____

_____

_____

_____

_____

_____

_____

_____

_____

_____

_____

_____

_____

_____

_____

_____

_____

_____

What's in your suitcase?

- More tissues
- Magnifying glass and binoculars to help spot triggers
- Choice – great choice, good choice, not so great choice
- Megaphone (for louder cheering!)
- Tissues
- Full length photo
- Album set up in your phone or on your computer where you will store your "becoming you" photos
- No Should Zone t-shirt and poster
- Your power
- Google maps
- Locks
- "Traffic Jam" written on an index card
- From www.youcanteatlove.com website, print off the "Stay" card
- Book of positive affirmations
- Seasoning
- Forgiveness
-

- Choices
- Community
- STOP
- Idea about your destination
- Plan for sabotagers
- Plan for food pushers
- Trash bags
- Oxygen mask
- WHY
- Friedrich Nietzsche quote
- Photo of you
- Index cards
- Stake
- Hammer
- www.youcanteatlove.com
- Snap a photo – post it to the You Can't Eat Love Facebook page
- Join the private You Can't Eat Love Facebook group
- Workbook
- *So, I said to myself…* Journal
- Pens
- Highlighters

Life Hacks

- One of the hardest sentences I had to learn to say was "I feel…". Then I ask myself "why am I feeling….?" As I got more practice saying this, the easier it was to recognize the triggers and ask myself why I was being "triggered". If switching my thought process, distracting myself or taking a short walk does not stop the "trigger", I will grab something high in protein – a protein drink (1st Phorm chocolate milkshake is my favorite), or a spoon full of peanut butter. The trick about peanut butter is I must close the jar and put it away before I eat the spoonful. I speak kindly to myself just as I would my very best friend in the whole wide world. (Don't ask me why, I just know that something high in protein stops the cravings from triggers faster than anything else I have tried. For me, the whole distraction thing becomes a fight of wills. And guess what wins.)

Jackie says

- Don't compare yourself to others
- Make sure you have a rest day

Travel Guides

- *Self-Compassion* by Kristin Neff, PhD[iii]

Section 3

Peeling Back the Layers

Motivation is like food for the brain.
You cannot get enough in one sitting.
It needs continual and regular top ups.

Peter Davies

Chapter 11

How Do We Get From Here to There

So, I was saying...

- Discovering which food plan you want to follow
- Tracking your food
- Substitutions
- Flavor is king
- Time saving cooking tools

And now, your turn...

List of weight loss plans and the pros and cons of each

Plan	Pros	Cons

Which plan are you choosing and why?

_____

_____

_____

_____

Brainstorm, Google, ask Alexa, explore ingredients you can substitute in your cooking:

Ingredient	Substitution
sour cream	Non-fat Greek yogurt

What's in your suitcase?

- Food plan/app
- Tracker – Fit and Food Journal is on Amazon https://www.amazon.com/dp/1736232207, you can download sample pages from www.youcanteatlove.com
- Refillable oil sprayers for olive oil and regular oil (I prefer the Misto brand)
- Food storage containers (my personal preference is the Rubbermaid Freshworks Produce Saver – they really work. Initial expense but you recover that in saved produce costs)
- More tissues
- Magnifying glass and binoculars to help spot triggers
- Choice – great choice, good choice, not so great choice
- Megaphone (for louder cheering!)
- Tissues
- Full length photo
- Album set up in your phone or on your computer where you will store your "becoming you" photos
- No Should Zone t-shirt and poster
- Your power

- Google maps
- Locks
- "Traffic Jam" written on an index card
- From www.youcanteatlove.com website, print off the "Stay" card
- Book of positive affirmations
- Seasoning
- Forgiveness
- Choices
- Community
- STOP
- Idea about your destination
- Plan for sabotagers
- Plan for food pushers
- Trash bags
- Oxygen mask
- WHY
- Friedrich Nietzsche quote
- Photo of you
- Index cards
- Stake
- Hammer
- www.youcanteatlove.com
- Snap a photo – post it to the You Can't Eat Love Facebook page
- Join the private You Can't Eat Love Facebook group
- Workbook
- *So, I said to myself...* Journal
- Pens
- Highlighters

Life Hacks

- Writing activates a different part of your brain and we are teaching our brain new tricks and habits
- I learned to cut out oil when sauteing onions, bell peppers, mushrooms and other veggies. I put them in the skillet and add 2-4 Tbsps of water, the water will begin cooking the veggies, stir occasionally. The veggies will release their liquid. Cook until no liquid remains in the skillet, proceed with your recipe.
- When the recipe calls for browning meat in oil, pat the meat dry, spray with oil, season, rub all over the meat then put it into the hot pan (non-stick skillets don't brown as well as regular pans)
- Buttermilk substitute – ¾ C yogurt mixed with ¼ C milk (I use non-fat Greek yogurt and ultra-filtered milk because there is no fat and I get extra protein.
- Pineapple cutter/corer (I use this at least once a week)
- I still weigh and measure everything. My scale is where I can grab it easily. Comes in very handy for baking. Don't guess – weigh and measure.
- Air fryer
- Small food processor
- Slow cooker or Instapot

Jackie says

- Track your food. If your nutrition is not right, you will not reach your goal
- Prioritize protein

Travel Guides

- Template for substitutions on www.youcanteatlove.com
- My favorite cookbooks – America's Test Kitchen *One Pan Wonders*[iv] and *Air Fryer Perfection*[v]. Shop on their website shop.americastestkitchen.com for the best pricing
- The Weight Loss Code by Yemi Fadipe[vi]

Chapter 12

Greens, Greens, And More Greens

So, I was saying...

- Menu planning
- Grocery shopping
- Placing orders for pickup
- Throwing food away
- Time out for misbehaving
- Setting up for success

And now, your turn...

More stuff to download! (Hope you stocked up on ink)

Sample menus and blank template

Sample menu plan and blank template

Sample grocery list and blank template

Here we are going to list the foods that do not know how to behave when they are in our house. Writing them down helps you be more aware of them and keeps me and myself from hiding them from you.

_____

_____

_____

_____

What do you need to do to be kind to yourself?

_____

_____

_____

_____

Let's come up with a plan to handle food that does not know how to behave itself. What are some actions/steps to take so you can make the best choice for the moment. Remember to cheer really loudly! Mark this page so you can refer to it each day.

_____

_____

_____

_____

_____

_____

_____

_____

_____

_____

_____

_____

_____

_____

_____

_____

_____

_____

_____

_____

_____

_____

_____

_____

What's in your suitcase?

- Bigger megaphone
- Menu plan
- Grocery list
- More trash bags
- Hug from me
- Food plan/app
- Tracker – Fit and Food Journal
- Refillable oil sprayers for olive oil and regular oil (I prefer the Misto brand)
- Food storage containers (my personal preference is the Rubbermaid Freshworks Produce Saver – they really work. Initial expense but you recover that in saved produce costs)
- More tissues
- Magnifying glass and binoculars to help spot triggers
- Choice – great choice, good choice, not so great choice
- Megaphone (for louder cheering!)
- Tissues
- Full length photo

- Album set up in your phone or on your computer where you will store your "becoming you" photos
- No Should Zone t-shirt and poster

- Your power
- Google maps
- Locks
- "Traffic Jam" written on an index card
- From www.youcanteatlove.com website, print off the "Stay" card
- Book of positive affirmations
- Seasoning
- Forgiveness
- Choices
- Community
- STOP
- Idea about your destination
- Plan for sabotagers
- Plan for food pushers
- Trash bags
- Oxygen mask
- WHY
- Friedrich Nietzsche quote
- Photo of you
- Index cards
- Stake
- Hammer
- www.youcanteatlove.com
- Snap a photo – post it to the You Can't Eat Love Facebook page
- Join the private You Can't Eat Love Facebook group
- Workbook
- *So, I said to myself...* Journal
- Pens
- Highlighters

Life Hacks

- Shop the perimeter of the store
- Place a pick up order about 5-7 days out from your grocery shopping day
- Homemade pasta (higher in protein and tastes so much better than store bought) 10 ounces of flour and 3 room-temperature LARGE (not extra-large) eggs. I make mine in the food processor. (Flour in first, pulse about 5 times, then add eggs and process until it starts sticking together. Remove from processor and knead until smooth, wrap in plastic wrap and let it sit, continue as with handmade.) It can be made by pouring the flour into a mound on a cutting surface (I am lazy so I will do it on parchment paper or some type of cling wrap), make a well in the middle, lightly scramble the eggs, pour into the well. Using a knife or chopstick start pulling the flour in and mixing it with the egg. After you have pulled all of the flour in, knead the dough til it feels smooth. Wrap in plastic wrap and let it sit for at least 30 minutes. Then you can cut into 4-5 pieces and roll then cut each section into strips one at a time. Boil in well salted water for about 2.5-3 minutes, drain and toss with about 1-2T of olive oil or other seasonings, add protein and serve.
- FAIL – Rethink what you hear. Now, I want you to hear First Attempt In Learning. Give yourself grace and kindness. FAIL is now shorthand and a signal to you that it is a First Attempt In Learning, tomorrow or next time will be better. You never really fail (see the difference in how the word is written?) until you quit. Don't quit. I believe in you.

Jackie says

- Master fundamental moves like squats and lunges

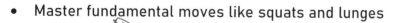

Travel Guides

- Templates for grocery lists and menu plans

Chapter 13

To Move Or Not To Move, That Is The Question

So, I was saying...

- Exercise
- Getting inefficient
- Start where *you* are and add just a bit each week
- Adding exercise
- You do you

And now, your turn...

Ways to add steps to your day: planned inefficiency!

- Park in the back of the parking lot
- Multiple trips to unload dryer
- Multiple trips to unload groceries
- Multiple trips to unload dishwasher
- Now, your turn!

_____

_____

_____

_____

_____

❖ Walking – where can you walk?

_____

_____

❖ How long do you know you can walk at the beginning of this journey?

_____

_____

❖ When can you walk?

_____

_____

❖ Who are you going to walk with (walking by yourself is ok too!)?

_____

_____

❖ How many times a week are you going to walk?

_____

_____

❖ Make a date with yourself – create reminders in your phone or on your
calendar_____

_____

Be sure to record your activity in the Fit and Food Journal!

Once you have decided all of this and made the date with yourself – let us know
in the Facebook group so we can celebrate with you!

Check out YouTube for beginning exercises. Remember to meet you where you
are today. Tomorrow, you will be somewhere else.

Celebration!!!

_____

_____

_____

_____

_____

_____

_____

_____

_____

_____

_____

_____

_____

_____

What's in your suitcase?

- Rubber boots
- Raincoat
- Exercises for beginners
- Health app or fitness tracker
- Timer (a lot of phones have a timer)
- Alarm set to remind you to go out and walk
- Headphones/music or podcasts
- Bigger megaphone
- Menu plan
- Grocery list
- More trash bags
- Hug from me
- Food plan/app
- Tracker – Fit and Food Journal is on Amazon, you can download sample pages from www.youcanteatlove.com
- Refillable oil sprayers for olive oil and regular oil (I prefer the Misto brand)
- Food storage containers (my personal preference is the Rubbermaid Freshworks Produce Saver – they really work. Initial expense but you recover that in saved produce costs)
- More tissues
- Magnifying glass and binoculars to help spot triggers
- Choice – great choice, good choice, not so great choice
- Megaphone (for louder cheering!)
- Tissues
- Full length photo

- Album set up in your phone or on your computer where you will store your "becoming you" photos
- No Should Zone t-shirt and poster
- Your power
- Google maps
- Locks
- "Traffic Jam" written on an index card
- From www.youcanteatlove.com website, print off the "Stay" card
- Book of positive affirmations
- Seasoning
- Forgiveness
- Choices
- Community
- STOP
- Idea about your destination
- Plan for sabotagers
- Plan for food pushers
- Trash bags
- Oxygen mask
- WHY
- Friedrich Nietzsche quote
- Photo of you
- Index cards
- Stake
- Hammer
- www.youcanteatlove.com
- Snap a photo – post it to the You Can't Eat Love Facebook page
- Join the private You Can't Eat Love Facebook group
- Workbook

- *So, I said to myself...* Journal
- Pens

- Highlighters

Life Hacks

- Being inefficient is a painless way to increase your activity.
- Make appointments with yourself just like you do for any other activity in your life. Make the time sacred. Oxygen Mask – use it
- Set a time for how long you are going to move and then add 1 minute each week.

Jackie says

- Invest in a great pair of shoes! (NoBull are my favorites)

Travel Guides

- Fit and Food Journal
  https://www.amazon.com/dp/1736232207
- *6-Minute Fitness at 60+: Simple Home Exercises to Reclaim Strength, Balance, and Energy in 15 Days*[vii] by Jonathan Su

Chapter 14

I Don't Want To Be The Rock

So, I was saying...

- Joining a gym
- Finding a trainer
- Making appointments with yourself

And now, your turn...

What is your gym why?

_____
_____
_____
_____
_____

Does it line up with your WHY?

_____
_____
_____
_____
_____
_____
_____

List of gyms you will be checking out:

Gym	# Guest Pass Days	How was it?

Your decision!

_____

List of trainers you will be checking out:

Trainer	What did you see?

Your choice?

_____

Date set for free session:

What are your workout goals?

_____
_____
_____
_____
_____

Don't forget to enter your workout plans in your Fit and Food Journal!

What's in your suitcase?

- Fanny pack or phone holder if you don't have cordless headphones
- Gym membership
- Date for Free Session
- Quality workout shoes
- Rubber boots
- Raincoat
- Exercises for beginners
- Health app or fitness tracker
- Timer (a lot of phones have a timer)
- Alarm set to remind you to go out and walk
- Headphones/music or podcasts
- Bigger megaphone
- Menu plan
- Grocery list
- More trash bags
- Hug from me
- Food plan/app
- Tracker – Fit and Food Journal
- Refillable oil sprayers for olive oil and regular oil (I prefer the Misto brand)
- Food storage containers (my personal preference is the Rubbermaid Freshworks Produce Saver – they really work. Initial expense but you recover that in saved produce costs)
- More tissues
- Magnifying glass and binoculars to help spot triggers
- Choice – great choice, good choice, not so great choice
- Megaphone (for louder cheering!)
- Tissues
- Full length photo
- Album set up in your phone or on your computer where you will store your "becoming you" photos
- No Should Zone t-shirt and poster
- Your power
- Google maps
- Locks
- "Traffic Jam" written on an index card
- From www.youcanteatlove.com website, print off the "Stay" card
- Book of positive affirmations
- Seasoning
- Forgiveness
- Choices
- Community
- STOP
- Idea about your destination
- Plan for sabotagers
- Plan for food pushers
- Trash bags
- Oxygen mask
- WHY
- Friedrich Nietzsche quote
- Photo of you
- Index cards
- Stake
- Hammer
- www.youcanteatlove.com
- Snap a photo – post it to the You Can't Eat Love Facebook page
- Join the private You Can't Eat Love Facebook group

- Workbook
- *So, I said to myself...* Journal
- Pens
- Highlighters

Life Hacks

- You can explore a gym before joining
- Some gyms offer a discount/specials for people over a certain age
- Some insurance companies will cover a gym membership
- Set appointments/reminders for all activity including walks and the gym

Jackie says

- A good trainer is focused
- A good trainer asks you a lot of questions

Travel Guides

- Fit and Food Journal

Chapter 15

There Is A Reason They Give Stars To Kindergartners

So, I was saying...

- Rewarding what we want to continue
- Ignoring what we want to stop
- Decide on rewards ahead of time so you focus on the reward
- The games we play

And now, your turn...

 Choices that you make and would like to change (like always ordering a large fry with your hamburger, or putting cream in your coffee)

Decide and write down how you are going to celebrate when you are successful (and yes, close to successful does count!)

_____
_____
_____
_____
_____
_____
_____
_____
_____
_____
_____

Here is a chance for you to write down goals you want to accomplish AND decide how you are going to reward yourself (not every goal is about losing weight, some are about behavior and habits you want to build. That whole make your brain happy thing. 😊) As you write down each goal be sure to think about why you are setting that goal. (some examples are lose 5lbs, walk 10 minutes 2 times this week, use non-fat greek yogurt on my fish taco instead of sour cream)

_____
_____
_____
_____
_____
_____
_____
_____
_____
_____
_____
_____
_____
_____
_____
_____
_____
_____
_____
_____
_____
_____
_____
_____
_____
_____

It's a confetti parade!!

What's in your suitcase?

- Star stickers
- Fun stickers
- Fanny pack or phone holder if you don't have cordless headphones
- Gym membership
- Date for Free Session
- Quality workout shoes
- Rubber boots
- Raincoat
- Exercises for beginners
- Health app or fitness tracker
- Timer (a lot of phones have a timer)
- Alarm set to remind you to go out and walk
- Headphones/music or podcasts
- Bigger megaphone
- Menu plan
- Grocery list
- More trash bags
- Hug from me
- Food plan/app
- Tracker – Fit and Food Journal
- Refillable oil sprayers for olive oil and regular oil (I prefer the Misto brand)
- Food storage containers (my personal preference is the Rubbermaid Freshworks Produce Saver – they really work. Initial expense but you recover that in saved produce costs)
- More tissues
- Magnifying glass and binoculars to help spot triggers
- Choice – great choice, good choice, not so great choice
- Megaphone (for louder cheering!)
- Tissues
- Full length photo
- Album set up in your phone or on your computer where you will store your "becoming you" photos
- No Should Zone t-shirt and poster
- Your power
- Google maps
- Locks
- "Traffic Jam" written on an index card
- From www.youcanteatlove.com website, print off the "Stay" card
- Book of positive affirmations
- Seasoning
- Forgiveness
- Choices
- Community
- STOP
- Idea about your destination
- Plan for sabotagers
- Plan for food pushers
- Trash bags
- Oxygen mask
- WHY
- Friedrich Nietzsche quote
- Photo of you
- Index cards
- Stake
- Hammer
- www.youcanteatlove.com

- Snap a photo – post it to the You Can't Eat Love Facebook page
- Join the private You Can't Eat Love Facebook group
- Workbook

- *So, I said to myself...* Journal
- Pens
- Highlighters

Life Hacks

- Buy some poster board or just get a piece of paper and create a chart of behaviors you want to change – each day you are successful – put up a sticker and do a happy dance! It's all about driving down that muddy road and making new ruts.
- Set goals each week AND decide on how you are going to reward yourself when you accomplish the goal. Set yourself up for success.
- If you don't reach your goal that week, keep the same goal and the same reward and refocus on the reward. You will get there!
- If a goal seems too big or too unreachable – break it down. I call it swiss cheesing something. Take one bite at a time, eventually it will all be gone.

Jackie says

- Focus on perfect form and posture
- Don't be afraid to ask questions or to ask for help

Travel Guides

- Books or sheets of stickers

Chapter 16

Eeny, Meeny, Miney, Moe

So, I was saying...

- Notice when making good and great choices
- Practice choices and forgiveness
- Celebrate *all* wins – no win is too small
- Keep your power
- Focus on "I feel" statements
- Cards and letters

And now, your turn...

Think about the last time you made a not so great choice.

_____

_____

Now, give yourself some empathy and a bit of sympathy – ("of course you "fill in the blank" because you were "fill in the blank".)

_____

_____

_____

_____

_____

_____

_____

How did you take care of yourself after you sat in your feeling?

_____
_____
_____
_____
_____
_____

How did that feel?

_____
_____
_____
_____

What would you like to differently next time?

_____
_____
_____
_____

How will you celebrate?

_____
_____
_____
_____

How is your thinking changing as you focus on your success and forgive your not so great choices?

_____
_____
_____
_____
_____
_____
_____
_____
_____
_____

Practice (put this on an index card or 3 or 5 and keep it handy):

I feel

_____
_____
_____
_____
_____
_____
_____
_____
_____
_____
_____

because_____

_____
_____
_____
_____
_____
_____
_____
_____
_____
_____
_____
_____
_____
_____
_____
_____
_____

What's in your suitcase?

- Plan for after you make a not so great choice
- Protein Powder/Drink (my favorite is 1ˢᵗ Phorm Chocolate Milkshake)
- Greeting Cards
- Star stickers
- Fun stickers
- Fanny pack or phone holder if you don't have cordless headphones
- Gym membership
- Date for Free Session
- Quality workout shoes
- Rubber boots
- Raincoat
- Exercises for beginners
- Health app or fitness tracker
- Timer (a lot of phones have a timer)
- Alarm set to remind you to go out and walk
- Headphones/music or podcasts
- Bigger megaphone
- Menu plan
- Grocery list
- More trash bags
- Hug from me
- Food plan/app
- Tracker – Fit and Food Journal
- Refillable oil sprayers for olive oil and regular oil (I prefer the Misto brand)
- Food storage containers (my personal preference is the Rubbermaid Freshworks Produce Saver – they really work. Initial expense but you

- recover that in saved produce costs)
- More tissues
- Magnifying glass and binoculars to help spot triggers
- Choice – great choice, good choice, not so great choice
- Megaphone (for louder cheering!)
- Tissues
- Full length photo
- Album set up in your phone or on your computer where you will store your "becoming you" photos
- No Should Zone t-shirt and poster
- Your power
- Google maps
- Locks
- "Traffic Jam" written on an index card
- From www.youcanteatlove.com website, print off the "Stay" card
- Book of positive affirmations
- Seasoning
- Forgiveness
- Choices
- Community
- STOP
- Idea about your destination
- Plan for sabotagers
- Plan for food pushers
- Trash bags
- Oxygen mask
- WHY
- Friedrich Nietzsche quote

- Photo of you
- Index cards
- Stake
- Hammer
- www.youcanteatlove.com
- Snap a photo – post it to the You Can't Eat Love Facebook page
- Join the private You Can't Eat Love Facebook group
- Workbook
- *So, I said to myself...* Journal
- Pens
- Highlighters

Life Hacks

- Feelings. This was the hardest part of my journey. Becoming unafraid to face my real feelings and learning how to safely express myself. Sorting out the pieces and parts of anger. So many times I was told not to feel or I couldn't feel or even worse I shouldn't fee and I believed those people. Now I know as a healthy human I MUST feel or I am not able to live my very best life. If this is hard for you, just reach out. I will listen.
- Celebrating the things we want to continue helps deepen the ruts in our brains
- No one can make you anything. Don't give away your power.
- Focus on behavior and not person (including yourself)
- Letters/cards from your bff help encourage you on the journey

Jackie says

- A good trainer is passionate
- A good trainer is relatable

Travel Guides

- *The Dance of Anger*[viii] by Harriet Lerner PhD
- *The Dance of Connection*[ix] by Harriet Lerner PhD

Chapter 17

Progress Not Perfection

So, I was saying...

- Rome was not built in a day
- Progress
- Mile markers
- Get rid of baggy clothes
- Take photos of yourself
- Bags of dog food – carry them!

And now, your turn...

What are your mile markers?

_____
_____
_____
_____

How are you tracking your progress and your successes?

_____
_____
_____
_____
_____

What are you doing to celebrate your progress (physical, mental and emotional progress)?

_____
_____
_____
_____
_____
_____
_____
_____
_____
_____
_____
_____

What's in your suitcase?

- Progress not perfection
- Bag/Trash bag for clothes that don't fit
- Woven belt
- Photo taken about the same date each month – put in a folder on your phone or computer
- Dog food 😊
- Happy Dance music!!
- Plan for after you make a not so great choice
- Protein Powder/Drink (my favorite is 1st Phorm Chocolate Milkshake)
- Greeting Cards
- Star stickers
- Fun stickers
- Fanny pack or phone holder if you don't have cordless headphones
- Gym membership
- Date for Free Session
- Quality workout shoes
- Rubber boots
- Raincoat
- Exercises for beginners
- Health app or fitness tracker
- Timer (a lot of phones have a timer)
- Alarm set to remind you to go out and walk
- Headphones/music or podcasts
- Bigger megaphone
- Menu plan
- Grocery list
- More trash bags
- Hug from me

- Food plan/app
- Tracker – Fit and Food Journal
- Refillable oil sprayers for olive oil and regular oil (I prefer the Misto brand)
- Food storage containers (my personal preference is the Rubbermaid Freshworks Produce Saver – they really work. Initial expense but you recover that in saved produce costs)
- More tissues
- Magnifying glass and binoculars to help spot triggers
- Choice – great choice, good choice, not so great choice
- Megaphone (for louder cheering!)
- Tissues
- Full length photo
- Album set up in your phone or on your computer where you will store your "becoming you" photos
- No Should Zone t-shirt and poster
- Your power
- Google maps
- Locks
- "Traffic Jam" written on an index card
- From www.youcanteatlove.com website, print off the "Stay" card
- Book of positive affirmations
- Seasoning
- Forgiveness
- Choices

- Community
- STOP
- Idea about your destination
- Plan for sabotagers
- Plan for food pushers
- Trash bags
- Oxygen mask
- WHY
- Friedrich Nietzsche quote
- Photo of you
- Index cards
-

- Stake
- Hammer
- www.youcanteatlove.com
- Snap a photo – post it to the You Can't Eat Love Facebook page
- Join the private You Can't Eat Love Facebook group
- Workbook
- *So, I said to myself…* Journal
- Pens
- Highlighters

Life Hacks

- If the journey is feeling overwhelming, look back at how far you have come. Look over your tracker and see the positive changes you have been making. Look at your photos and enjoy seeing you being revealed.
- Don't keep any clothes that either don't fit or that you don't feel amazing in when you put them on
- Buckle your belt to the side
- Taking a photo the about the same date each month helps our brains repaint how it sees us. Don't be afraid to take more than one a month. It will help your brain realize a new you is here and the old you is gone.

Jackie says

- A good trainer walks the walk

Travel Guides

- *Self-Compassion*[iii] by Kristin Neff PhD
- *So, I said to myself…* Journal

Chapter 18

You Don't Have To Do This Alone

So, I was saying...

- The power to choose
- Take control
- Resources

And now, your turn...

How are you taking responsibility for your feelings?

_____

_____

_____

_____

_____

Are there people in your life that are not embracing the "new you"? If yes, list them here.

_____

_____

_____

_____

_____

_____

How can you respond or ignore (ignore is ALWAYS a choice) their unhelpful comments?

_____
_____
_____
_____
_____
_____
_____
_____
_____

We are back to your "dug down really deep" WHY. If you haven't already, make lots of copies of your WHY and put them where you are reminded. Go ahead and write it out again, right here.

_____
_____
_____
_____
_____
_____
_____
_____
_____
_____
_____
_____
_____
_____
_____

What's in your suitcase?

- A breath, a moment, a pause
- Book of Affirmations or Inspirations
- BHAW (Big Hairy Amazing WHY)
- Self-Compassion[iii] by Kristin Neff PhD
- More pens and highlighters
- Miracle Morning[i] – help get your day started with a great mindset
- Progress not perfection
- Bag/Trash bag for clothes that don't fit
- Woven belt
- Photo taken about the same date each month – put in a folder on your phone or computer
- Dog food 😊
- Happy Dance music!!
- Plan for after you make a not so great choice
- Protein Powder/Drink (my favorite is 1st Phorm Chocolate Milkshake)
- Greeting Cards
- Star stickers
- Fun stickers
- Fanny pack or phone holder if you don't have cordless headphones
- Gym membership
- Date for Free Session
- Quality workout shoes
- Rubber boots
- Raincoat
- Exercises for beginners
- Health app or fitness tracker

- Timer (a lot of phones have a timer)
- Alarm set to remind you to go out and walk
- Headphones/music or podcasts
- Bigger megaphone
- Menu plan
- Grocery list
- More trash bags
- Hug from me
- Food plan/app
- Tracker – Fit and Food Journal
- Refillable oil sprayers for olive oil and regular oil (I prefer the Misto brand)
- Food storage containers (my personal preference is the Rubbermaid Freshworks Produce Saver – they really work. Initial expense but you recover that in saved produce costs)
- More tissues
- Magnifying glass and binoculars to help spot triggers
- Choice – great choice, good choice, not so great choice
- Megaphone (for louder cheering!)
- Tissues
- Full length photo
- Album set up in your phone or on your computer where you will store your "becoming you" photos
- No Should Zone t-shirt and poster
- Your power

- Google maps
- Locks
- "Traffic Jam" written on an index card
- From www.youcanteatlove.com website, print off the "Stay" card
- Book of positive affirmations
- Seasoning
- Forgiveness
- Choices
- Community
- STOP
- Idea about your destination
- Plan for sabotagers
- Plan for food pushers
- Trash bags

- Oxygen mask
- WHY
- Friedrich Nietzsche quote
- Photo of you
- Index cards
- Stake
- Hammer
- www.youcanteatlove.com
- Snap a photo – post it to the You Can't Eat Love Facebook page
- Join the private You Can't Eat Love Facebook group
- Workbook
- *So, I said to myself...* Journal
- Pens
- Highlighters

Life Hacks

- I'm just curious...
- I hear you saying...
- Right now, I am working to bet the best me I can be.

Jackie says

- A good trainer listens to what you are saying
- A good trainer inspires you

Travel Guides

- *Self-Compassion*[iii] by Kristin Neff PhD
- *The Miracle Morning*[ix] by Hal Elrod
- *The Magic of Thinking Big*[x] by David J Schwartz
- *Boundaries*[xi] by Henry Cloud and John Townsend

Chapter 19

Very end? No, just the beginning

So, I was saying...

You have collected a lot of tools and tips on this journey. You may need some help getting your suitcase out of the car.

Remember to drive slowly to make sure you are making new ruts. Always stay in the car. Don't park it and don't walk home.

You know where you are going and more importantly, WHY.

And one last thing – You are amazing just as you are.

And now, your turn...

On this trip, what did you discover about your relationship with food?

_____
_____
_____
_____
_____
_____
_____
_____

What did you discover about the people around you?

_____
_____
_____
_____
_____
_____
_____
_____
_____

What did you discover about yourself?

_____
_____
_____
_____
_____
_____
_____
_____

How are you going to celebrate discovering you? (Share with us on Facebook!)

_____
_____
_____
_____
_____
_____

What's in your suitcase?

- A mirror, so you can see what I see. One amazing, strong person
- A breath, a moment, a pause
- Book of Affirmations or Inspirations
- BHAW (Big Hairy Amazing WHY)
- Self-Compassion[iii] by Kristin Neff PhD
- More pens and highlighters
- Miracle Morning[i] – help get your day started with a great mindset
- Progress not perfection
- Bag/Trash bag for clothes that don't fit
- Woven belt
- Photo taken about the same date each month – put in a folder on your phone or computer
- Dog food ☺
- Happy Dance music!!
- Plan for after you make a not so great choice
- Protein Powder/Drink (my favorite is 1st Phorm Chocolate Milkshake)
- Greeting Cards
- Star stickers
- Fun stickers
- Fanny pack or phone holder if you don't have cordless headphones
- Gym membership
- Date for Free Session
- Quality workout shoes
- Rubber boots
- Raincoat
- Exercises for beginners

- Health app or fitness tracker
- Timer (a lot of phones have a timer)
- Alarm set to remind you to go out and walk
- Headphones/music or podcasts
- Bigger megaphone
- Menu plan
- Grocery list
- More trash bags
- Hug from me
- Food plan/app
- Tracker – Fit and Food Journal
- Refillable oil sprayers for olive oil and regular oil (I prefer the Misto brand)
- Food storage containers (my personal preference is the Rubbermaid Freshworks Produce Saver – they really work. Initial expense but you recover that in saved produce costs)
- More tissues
- Magnifying glass and binoculars to help spot triggers
- Choice – great choice, good choice, not so great choice
- Megaphone (for louder cheering!)
- Tissues
- Full length photo
- Album set up in your phone or on your computer where you will store your "becoming you" photos
- No Should Zone t-shirt and poster

- Your power
- Google maps
- Locks
- "Traffic Jam" written on an index card
- From www.youcanteatlove.com website, print off the "Stay" card
- Book of positive affirmations
- Seasoning
- Forgiveness
- Choices
- Community
- STOP
- Idea about your destination
- Plan for sabotagers
- Plan for food pushers
- Trash bags

- Oxygen mask
- WHY
- Friedrich Nietzsche quote
- Photo of you
- Index cards
- Stake
- Hammer
- www.youcanteatlove.com
- Snap a photo – post it to the You Can't Eat Love Facebook page
- Join the private You Can't Eat Love Facebook group
- Workbook
- *So, I said to myself…* Journal
- Pens
- Highlighters

"When we are no longer able to change a situation, we are challenged to change ourselves."

Viktor Frankl

To schedule a free 15-minute clarity call with Leslie
go to www.youcanteatlove.com

References

_____

[ii]

[iii] Neff, Kristin, PhD. Self-Compassion: The Proven Power Of Being Kind To Yourself. New York: William Morrow, 2011.

[iv] America's Test Kitchen. Air Fryer Perfection: From Crispy Fries and Juicy Steaks To Perfect Vegetables. Boston: Penguin Random House Publisher Services, 2019.

[v] America's Test Kitchen. Cook's Country One-Pan Wonders: Fuss-Free Meals For Your Sheet Pan, Dutch Oven, Skillet, Roasting Pan, Casserole, And Slow Cooker. Brookline: Penguin Random House Publisher Services, 2017.

[vi] Fadipe, Yemi. The Weight Loss Code: A Practical Guide to Sustainable Weight Loss. 2020.

[vii] Su, Jonathan. 6-Minute Fitness at 60+: Simple Home Exercises to Reclaim Strength, Balance, and Energy in 15 Days. 2020.

[viii] Lerner, Harriet, PhD. The Dance of Anger: A Woman's Guide To Changing The Patterns Of Intimate Relationships. New York: William Morrow, 2014.

[ix] Lerner, Harriet, PhD. The Dance of Connection: How To Talk To Someone When You're Mad, Hurt, Scared, Frustrated, Insulted, Betrayed, or Desperate. New York: HarperCollins Publishers, 2002.

[x] Schwartz, David J. The Magic of Thinking Big. New York: Fireside Edition, 1987.

[xi] Cloud, Dr. Henry, & Townsend Dr John. Boundaries: When To Say Yes, How To Say No To Take Control of Your Life. Grand Rapids: Zondervan, 2017.

About the Author

Leslie Lindsey Davis is always on a journey. Her motto is "why not?". She measures things she wants to do against the yardstick of "When I am 80 years old, I don't want to be sitting in my rocking chair on my front porch saying, 'I wish I would have'".

She has taken a wrong turn on several trips with her older boys. The boys would say "we're lost". Her reply was always, "No, we are on an adventure."

Life is one grand adventurous journey and making sure everything is done from scuba diving to beekeeping. From riding on an elephant to riding in a hot air balloon. And so much more in between.

Her passions, besides her family, are GUTaS International and her heart family in Zimbabwe – especially Mercy, Betty and Itai. GUTaS stands for Get Up, Take a Step. GUTaS is changing lives one step, one stitch at a time.

When her husband and children ask "Why?" Her response is always "Why not."

If we have our own why in life,
we can get along with almost any how.

Friedrich Nietzsche

Made in the USA
Columbia, SC
17 February 2022

56377463R00052